Welcome to 'Higgledy Piggledy Jazz' for classical guitar ensemble.
Three classical guitar experts Philip Castledine, James Rippingale and Selina Copley have created Duets, Trios and Quartets for classical guitar ensemble based on my original ten pieces for piano. These new arrangements are suitable for players with various levels of ability ranging from Beginners to Intermediate as well as Advanced levels. The pieces are full of fun and I'm sure each member of the ensemble will enjoy playing them in lessons and recitals. Ensembles can be played with one or more players per part to create a larger group.

LIST OF PIECES

SUPER DUCK
Elena V. Cobb
arr. Philip Castledine
Opus 4 Nr 1
Swing 8's ♩ = 90 - 140
I
II
III
A
B
C
D
mf
f

E
F
G

I ATE ALL THE CHOC'LATE

Elena V. Cobb
arr. Philip Castledine
Opus 4 Nr 2

12
B
B

17

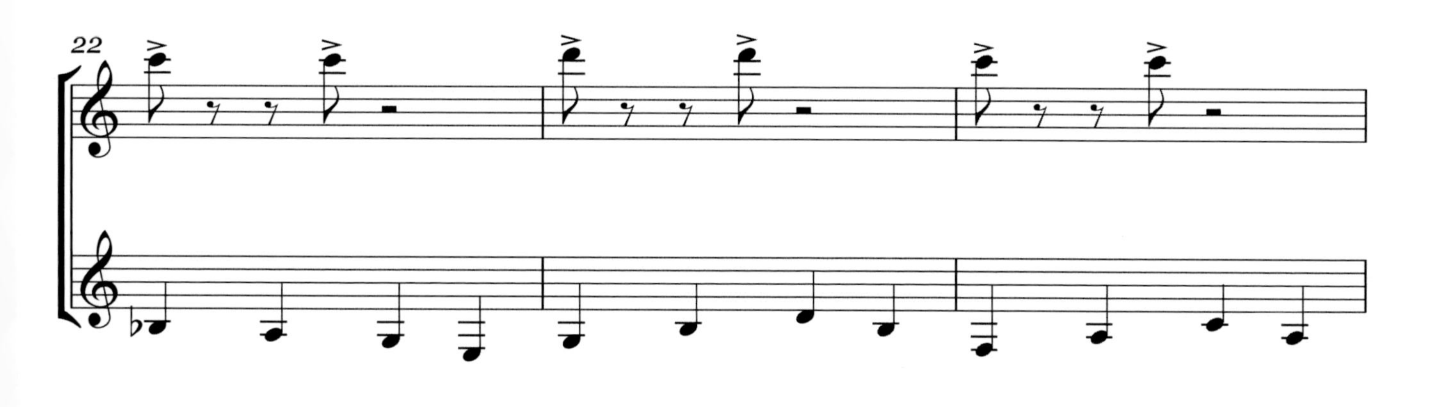
22

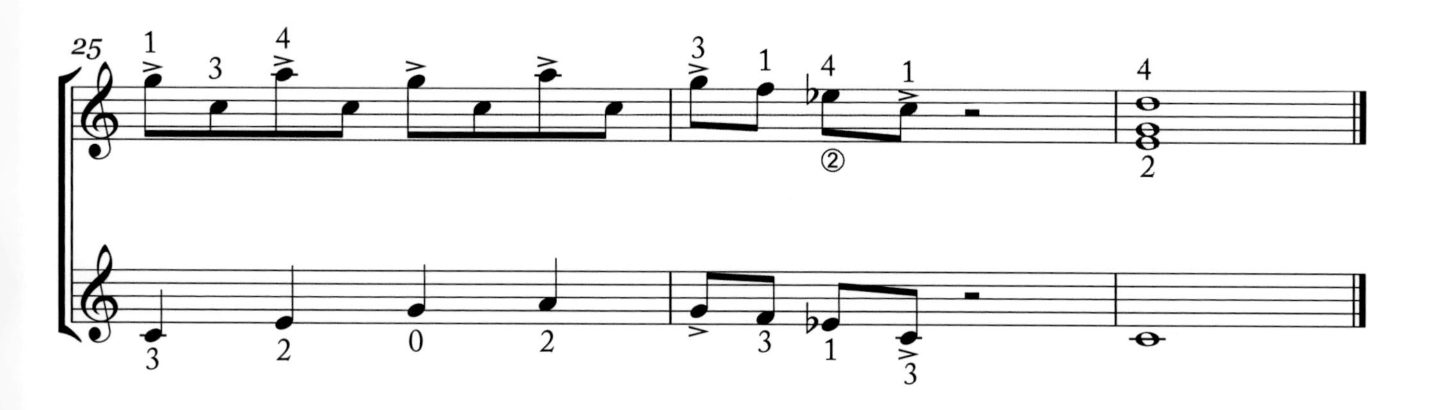
25

YOU TELL ME WHY I WAIT FOR CHRISTMAS?

Elena V. Cobb
arr.Philip Castledine
Opus 4 Nr 3

Rock ♩ = 65 - 140

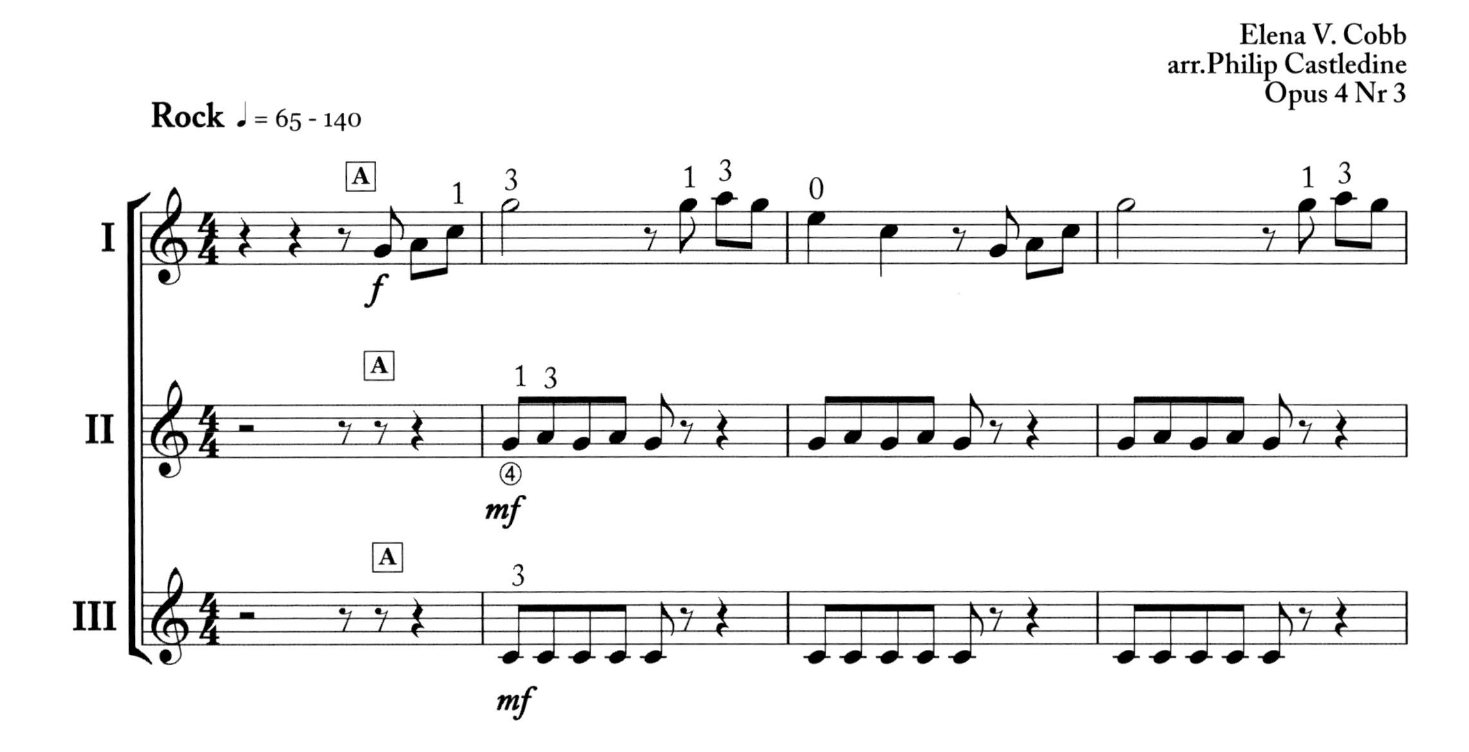

NERDY CAT'S TWIST

Elena V. Cobb
arr. Philip Castledine
Opus 4 Nr 4

Groovy Straight ♩ = 70 - 110

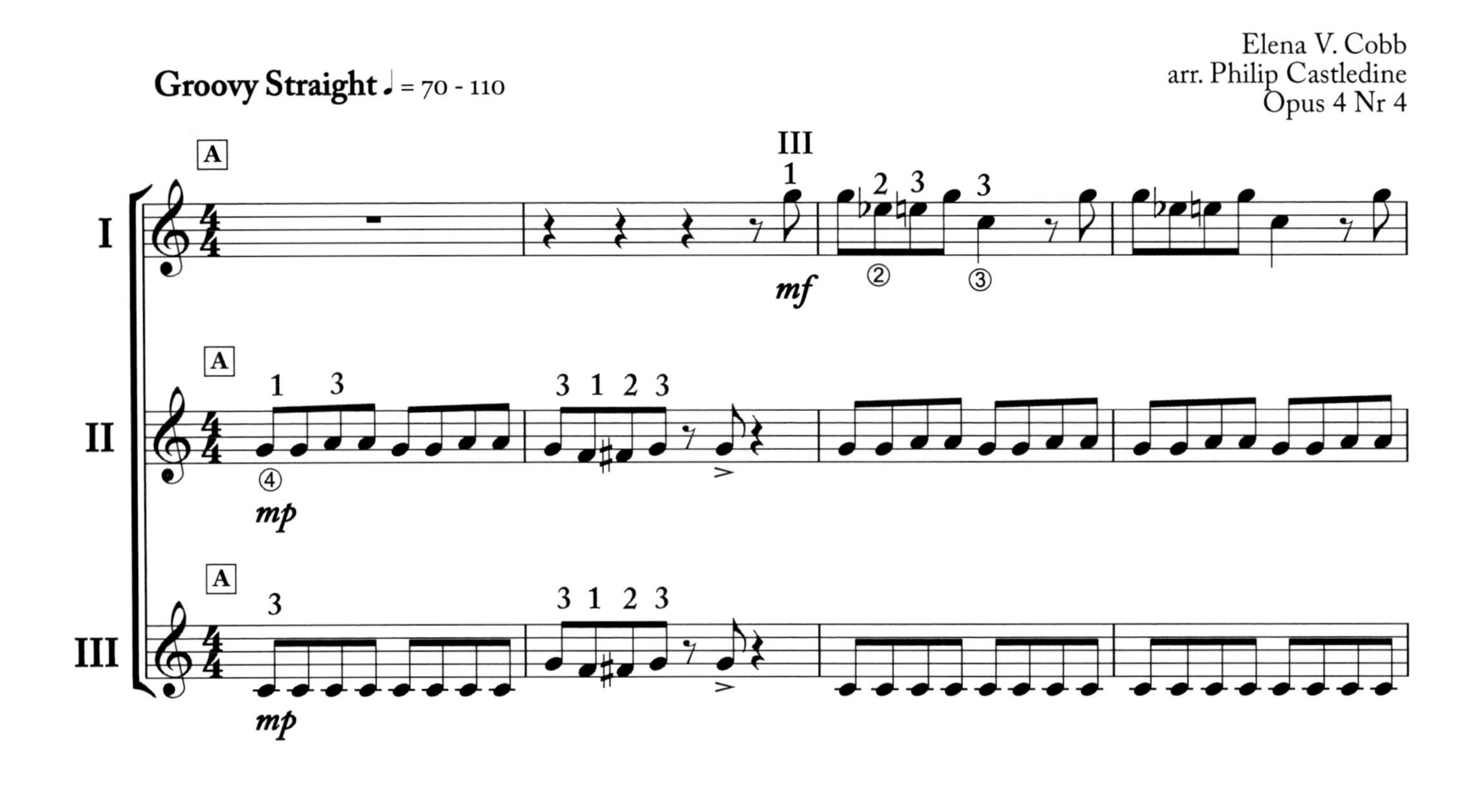

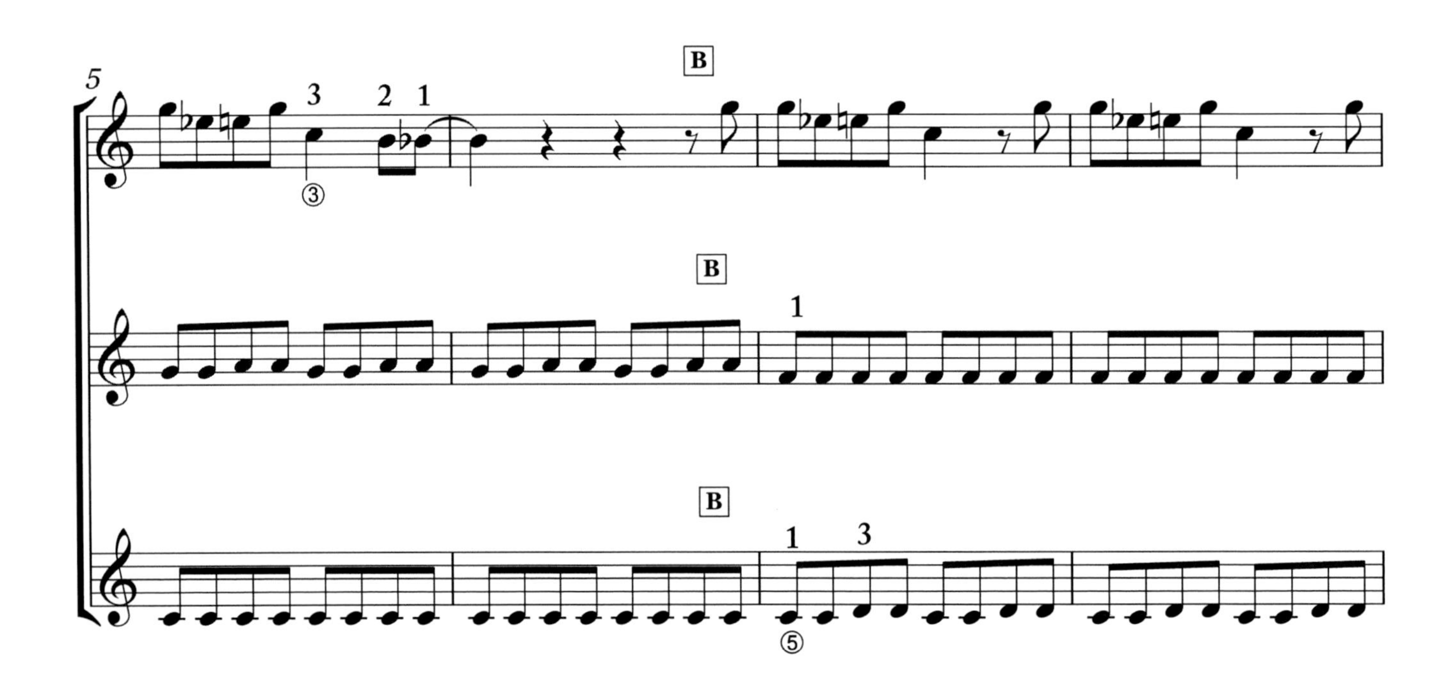

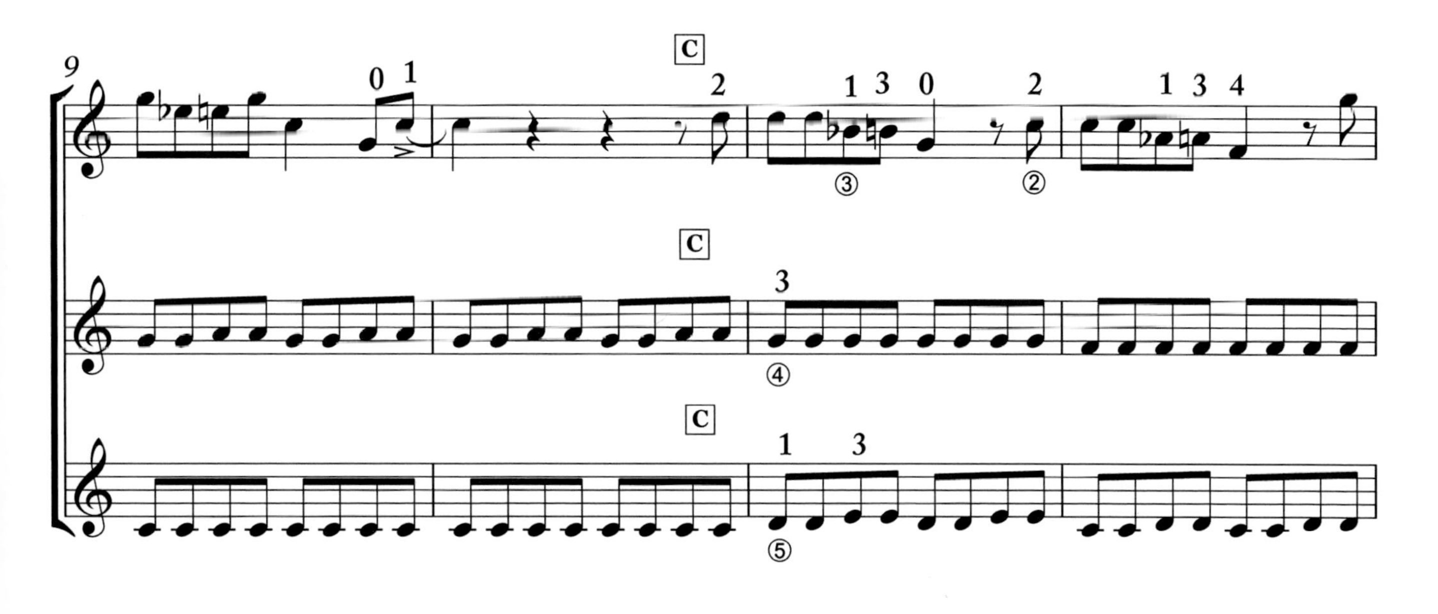
9
C
C
C

13
D
D
D

16

BLUES
FOR LITTLE PEOPLE

Elena V. Cobb
arr.Philip Castledine
Opus 4 Nr 5

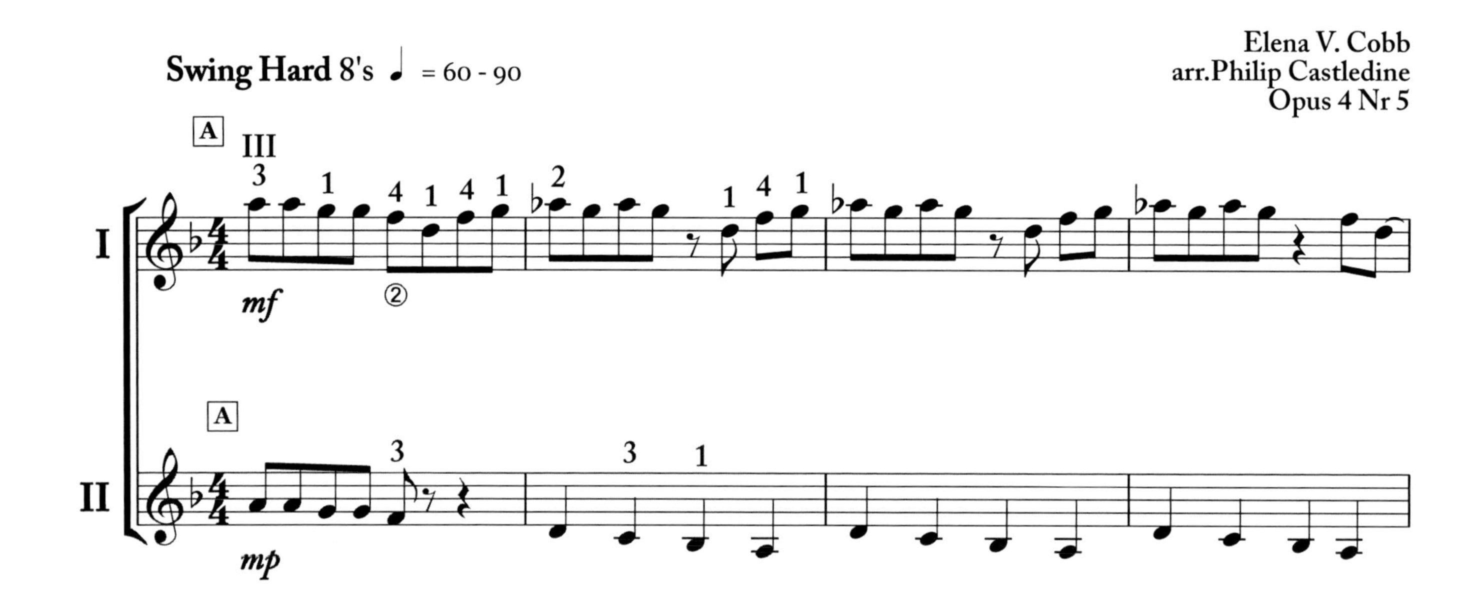

B
f
B
cresc.
mf

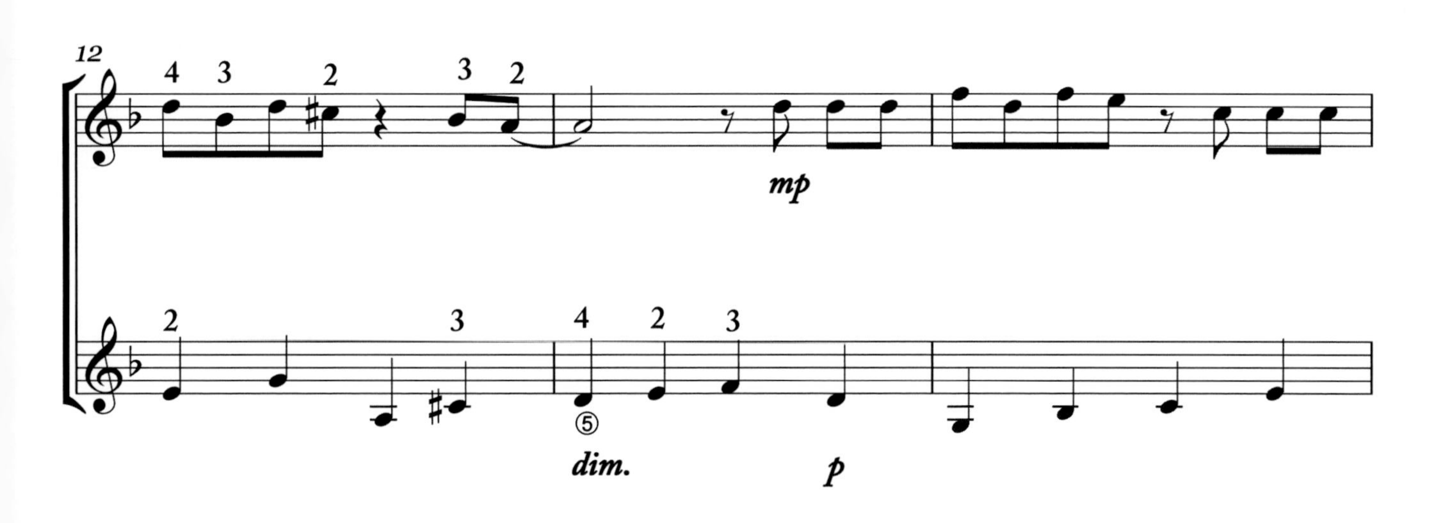
mp
dim.
p

cresc.
f
cresc.
f

TIME TO CATCH A TRAIN

Swing 8's ♩ = 90 - 145

Elena V. Cobb
arr. Philip Castledine
Opus 4 Nr 6

19
23
D
28
33
E
38
cresc.

POLKA BUTTERFLY

Elena V. Cobb
arr. Philip Castledine
Opus 4 Nr 7

21
D
mf
D
pp
mp
27
f
mf
33
E
mf
E
p
37

HIGGLEDY PIGGLEDY JAZZ

C
15
f
C
f
C
f
19
23

27 D

mf

D

mf

D

f

32

III

36

PEONY PINK

Elena V. Cobb
arr. Selina Copley
Opus 4 Nr 9

12
C
C
C
C
V
16
18
IV
I
III
I

21
D
XI
V
f
mf
25
E
28
I

30
F
mf
mp
34
G
37
dim
p
pp
VIII
CVIII
X

TAKE THREE / JAZZ WALTZ

With optional Double Bass or Bass Guitar part

Elena V. Cobb
arr. James Rippingale
Opus 4 Nr 10

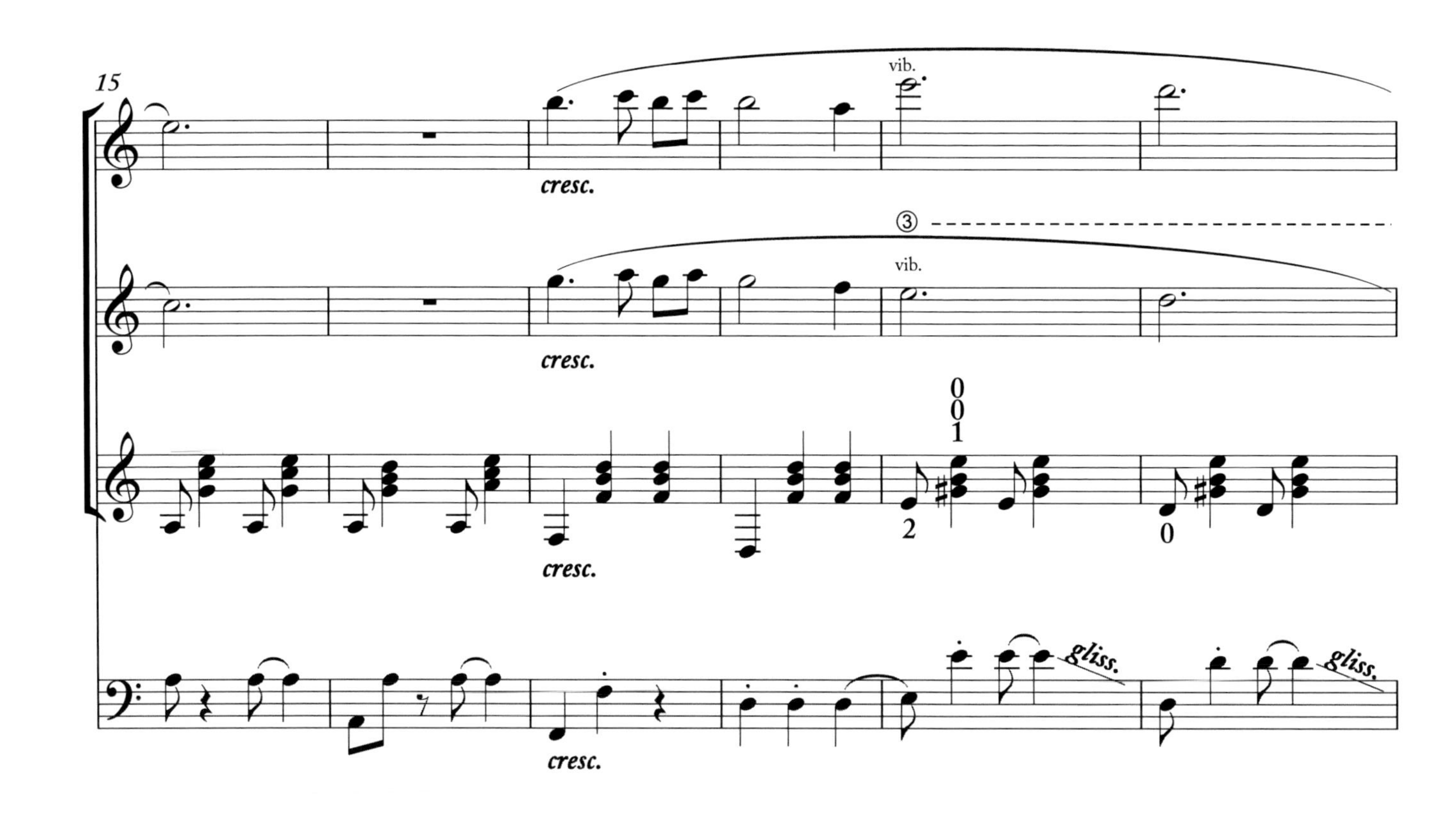
15
cresc.
vib.
cresc.
vib.
cresc.
gliss.
gliss.
cresc.

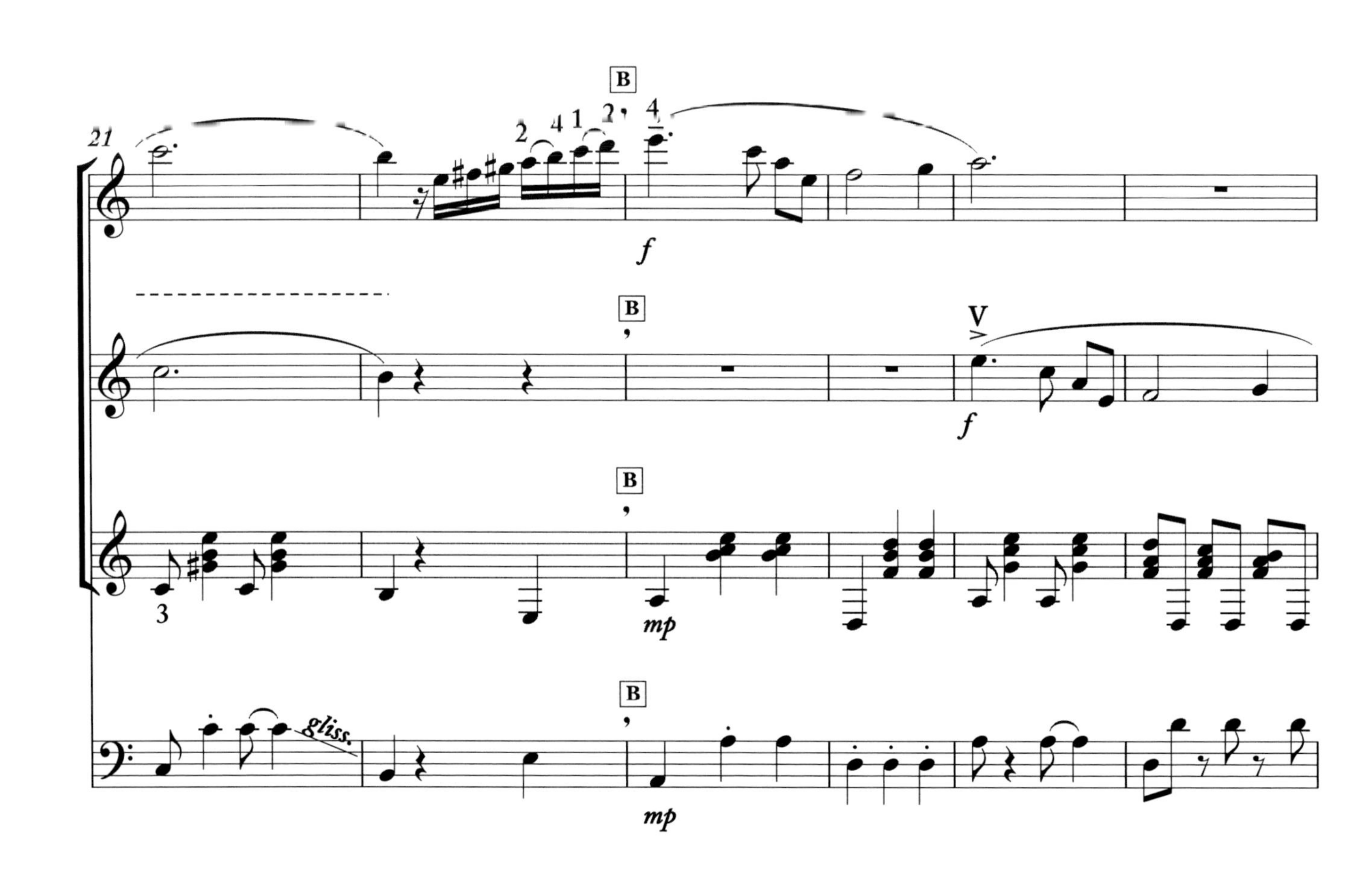
21
B
f
B
f
B
mp
gliss.
B
mp

27
mf
mp
mf
p
p

33
VII
dim.
gliss.
dim.
dim.

39
C
4
2
1
3
X
1
dim.
C
③
gliss.
③
gliss.
gliss.
C
C

44
XII
3
1
2
4
1
4
pp
③
gliss.
③
pp
pp
pp

NOTES

CONGRATULATIONS!

YOU HAVE BEEN AWARDED THE

HIGGLEDY PIGGLEDY

CERTIFICATE OF ACHIEVEMENT

Your Name ....

Teacher's Name ....

Date ....

Elena V Cobb x

www.evcmusicpublications.co.uk